BATTLE CHASERS: A GATHERING OF HEROES. Published by WildStorm Productions. Cover, design pages, and compilation © 1999 WildStorm Productions. BAT
CHASERS is ® & © 1999 Joe Madureira. All Rights Reserved. Originally published in single magazine form as BATTLE CHASERS PRELUDE, BATTLE CHASERS #
and FRANK FRAZETTA FANTASY ILLUSTRATED #2. Copyright © 1998, 1999 Joe Madureira. Cliffhanger Productions is a Trademark of WildStorm Productions, an imp
of DC Comics. Editorial offices: 7910 Ivanhoe, #438, La Jolla, CA 92037. Any similarities to persons living or dead is purely coincidental. PRINTED IN CANADA
DC Comics, a division of Warner Bros.– A Time Warner Entertainment Company

JOE MADUREIRA
Creator/Pencils/Story

MUNIER SHARRIEFF
Story

TOM McWEENEY
Inks

VINCE RUSSELL
Additional Inks (Pages 1-7)

LIQUID!
CHRISTIAN LICHTNER
ARON LUSEN
Colors

RICHARD STARKINGS
& COMICRAFT
Letters

KASEY REIS
Collected Edition Design

JOE MADUREIRA
TOM McWEENEY
LIQUID!
Dust Cover Illustration

this **Sherman tank**." Stuff like that. Animation was even MORE exciting to me. I had zero interest in movies which featured flesh and blood actors. Instead, I was racing to the TV to see if Tom would finally flatten Jerry, if the Road Runner would finally be caught in an Acme disaster, or if Scooby would unmask the villain of the day (make sure to check for a second mask Scooby! >whew<). Then one day, there he was... spinning a web, running up walls, knocking out some hideous Green Goblin. My friendly neighborhood Spider-Man!

I spent the next year trying to figure out how I could soak a spider in radio waves, and get it to bite me. I wanted to BE Spider-man. *Sigh.* Fortunately, I soon gave up on that idea, and just stuck to drawing him instead. I came up with all kinds of stories and villains for him. Little did I know there were books out there just like mine! They were called comic books!!! (Um, okay, so they weren't JUST like mine; the pages were stapled together, the stories made sense and the art was good! Sheesh! Gimme a break, I was only 7 years old!!!) Ahem.

Once I discovered comics, it was all over. For years, I lived and breathed comics. I would go so far as to starve in school, so

I could use my lunch-money to buy comics. I would get together with my friends after school, and we'd come up with our OWN characters, our OWN stories. Since I was the best 'drawer' (I love that term), I would put pencil to paper to make the stories come alive. But it wasn't super-hero comics we were creating. You see, all those visits to the comic store turned me on to something else. A little game by the name of *Dungeons & Dragons*. (Yeah, I know. *Geeeek.*)

For the rest of the 80's, my garage became a portal to another dimension for my friends and I. We gathered nightly with our characters and dice. Some of the stories that evolved during our sessions were really wild— more vivid and unpredictable than anything in a comic.

Suddenly, drawing was more fun than ever. I would fill all my sketchbooks with drawings of dragons, unicorns, elves, etc. Eventually, we stopped playing D&D (we discovered more important things, like girls), and I got back into comics. But when I sat down to draw, I still found myself drawing wizards and monsters instead of super-heroes like Spidey. I wondered why there were no comics set in a fantasy realm, with characters and creatures straight out of D&D. There were a few books that trickled onto the market, but for the most part, they seemed uninspired, or just poorly done. Having become quite serious about drawing, I enrolled myself at the High School of Art & Design in New York.

It was there at A&D that two of the most important events of my life would transpire. One was meeting a beautiful girl that would later become my wife. The other: receiving an internship at Marvel Comics!

Still hard for me to believe, but at the age of 16, while all of my classmates were still hitting the comic shops, I was WORKING in the Marvel Comics building! Granted, it was all intern work (making photo copies, filing, etc.), but I got all my comics for free. More importantly, I got to see first hand how comics were made! Even better, I was able to show my work to artists who hung around the office, getting tons of helpful advice from guys like John Romita, Mark Texeira, and even Jim Lee (though to this day, Jim doesn't remember). It wasn't long before I got some penciling work of my own, including the ultimate gig: a run on Marvel's *Uncanny X-men.*

The few years I spent on *Uncanny* were extremely important ones. It was there that I hit my stride, and developed a style of my own (up until then, my characters looked like emaciated Arthur Adams wannabe's). Towards the end of my run however, it was getting harder and harder to get the pages done. I was getting burnt out on drawing superhero comics. I was aching for something new. Though most of my friends and peers (not to mention common-sense) advised against it, I knew I had to set out on my own.

Fueled by that burning desire from my childhood to produce a comic based in a *Dungeons & Dragons* setting, I set out to create BATTLE CHASERS. Most people shuddered when I told them about it. Everyone knew fantasy based comics didn't do very well, especially in today's fickle market. Still, I knew I had to give it a shot. If there was ever a time in my career when I could attempt it, it was now. Amazingly, like a dream come true, the book was a hit! Readers embraced BATTLE CHASERS with open arms. To them, I am eternally grateful. I hope I've shed some light on the inspirations that lead to the creation of this book. Hopeful too, that other aspiring artists out there might find the courage to follow their dreams.

I would like to thank the incredibly talented people who helped make BATTLE CHASERS a reality. This book is dedicated to them. Munier, who's steady stream of over-the-top stories and ceaseless enthusiasm kept me glued to my desk (not to mention the phone…). Tom, who's inks bring out a quality in my work that I never knew was there. Thanks to Chris and Aron at Liquid!, long-time friends, and quite simply, the best colorists in the business. Just take a good look at these pages, and then pull out a comic from 3 years ago. What these guys have done for the medium is unbelievable. The same can be said for Richard Starkings, and his band of lettering madmen (and women!). Call me crazy, but I just think books are more fun to read when they receive the Comicraft treatment! I'd also like to thank my Cliffhanger cohorts Jeff and Humberto, Scott Dunbier, our patient (okay, not so patient) editor (I'm on the phone right now telling him he'll have this foreword by tomorrow…*Yeah right.*), as well as Jim Lee for getting us all together. Lastly I'd like to thank my loving wife Margaret, who is, and will always be, my greatest inspiration.

Thank you, and enjoy.

Joe Madureira

HIS QUAINT COTTAGE, NESTLED IN THE WOODLAND HILLS OF THORN'S GLEN, IS HOME TO THE GREAT *ARAMUS*, DECORATED MILITARY HERO AND PROTECTOR OF THE UNIFIED TERRITORIES.

ARAMUS, HOWEVER, HAS GONE MISSING, ALONG WITH A HANDFUL OF HIS FINEST MEN.

AFTER MONTHS OF FRUITLESS SEARCHING, THE REALIZATION HAS BEGUN TO SET IN

ARAMUS -- THE HUMAN WORLD'S MOST CHAMPIONED HERO --

-- IS GONE!

THIS NOTION, HOWEVER, IS NOT SHARED BY EVERYONE...

LEAST OF ALL *GULLY*, ARAMUS' YOUNG AND ONLY CHILD.

SHE TAKES COMFORT IN HER FATHER'S PRIVATE STUDY, AMIDST HIS BELONGINGS, HIS CLOAK PROVIDES A WARM EMBRACE...

...HIS WORDS PROVIDE A VOICE... AND PERHAPS EVEN... AN ANSWER!

IS THAT WHAT YOU'VE HAD TO DO, FATHER?

KRAKOOM

A Fool is One who Believes Retreat to be the Course of Rogues and Cowards. There will come a Time when the Enemy's Power is so Great, that Retreat will be your Only option. You must do this to draw the enemy Away from that which you have Sworn to Protect.

IS THAT WHY YOU'VE BEEN AWAY FOR SO LONG?

WAS THERE SOMETHING BIG AND HORRIBLE THAT THREATENED NANNY AND ME?

WHILE, DOWNSTAIRS...

STRANGE, THIS WEATHER. VERY UNUSUAL FOR THIS TIME OF YEAR...

PERHAPS THEY'LL NOT SHOW--

SILENCE WOMAN!

THEY COULD BE WATCHING!

IT WON'T BE LONG NOW!

MA'AM...

Y-YES?

...IS THERE ANYONE ELSE *HERE* THAT WE CAN *QUESTION*? A *FAMILY MEMBER* PERHAPS?

N-NO, I'M QUITE *ALONE* HERE.

REALLY?...

HEATHEN!

KATHLAM

MOVE AWAY FROM THE WOMAN OR I'LL KILL YOU WHERE YOU STAND!

AH, THE *ROYAL GUARD!* WE'RE ON THE SAME *SIDE* HERE. PERHAPS IF YOU'D LET ME *EXPLAIN...*

SILENCE YOUR *FORKED TONGUE!* YOU AND YOUR MEN ARE BEING PLACED UNDER ARREST!

WHOAH! WATCH WHERE YOU'RE WAVING THAT THING!

I SAID SILENCE! DON'T MOVE!

HUH-WHO ARE YOU?

SORRY FOR THE SCARE. IT COULD BE *DANGEROUS* FOR YOU DOWNSTAIRS. STAY IN YOUR ROOM UNTIL I CALL YOU OUT, OKAY?

'KAY.

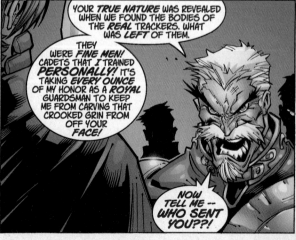

YOUR *TRUE NATURE* WAS REVEALED WHEN WE FOUND THE BODIES OF THE *REAL TRACKERS.* WHAT WAS *LEFT* OF THEM.

THEY WERE *FINE MEN!* CADETS THAT I TRAINED *PERSONALLY!* IT'S TAKING *EVERY OUNCE* OF MY HONOR AS A *ROYAL GUARDSMAN* TO KEEP ME FROM CARVING THAT *CROOKED GRIN* FROM OFF YOUR *FACE!*

NOW TELL ME -- WHO SENT YOU??!

TO FACE NORMAL MEN, PERHAPS...

...NOT NIGHTMARES!

THE WOMAN'S HASTENED ESCAPE DOES NOT GO UNDETECTED BY THE PACK LEADER'S ACUTE SENSE OF HEARING.

HUFF HUFF HUFF

OH PLEASE DEAR GOD!

HE HAD SUSPECTED THAT SHE WOULD BE THE ONE TO LEAD THEM TO WHAT THEY WERE TRULY AFTER.

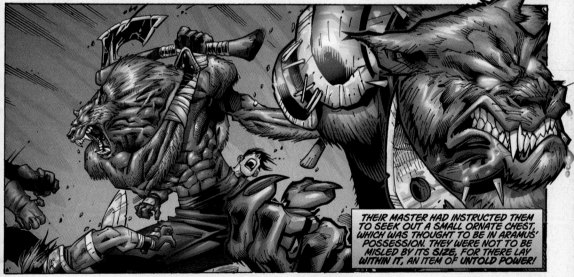

THEIR MASTER HAD INSTRUCTED THEM TO SEEK OUT A SMALL ORNATE CHEST, WHICH WAS THOUGHT TO BE IN ARAMUS' POSSESSION. THEY WERE NOT TO BE MISLED BY ITS SIZE, FOR THERE LAY WITHIN IT, AN ITEM OF UNTOLD POWER!

AND THEY WERE TO OBTAIN IT AT ANY PRICE!

GULLY! HURRY CHILD, THERE ISN'T MUCH TIME!

...

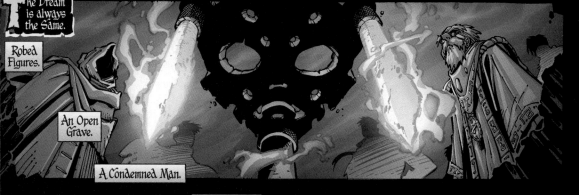

The Dream is always the Same.

Robed Figures.

An Open Grave.

A Condemned Man.

Mystic Armor.

Searing Heat.

Always the Same... Except the Screams. They get **Louder** every time.

HUH!!

STRANGE... EVERY TIME I'VE HAD THE DREAM BEFORE, THE OTHERS... THEIR FACES WERE *CLEAR* TO ME. BUT NOW... HMMM...

CALIBRETTO... YOU HERE?! WE NEED MORE WOOD FOR THE FIRE.

AGH! WHERE DID HE RUN OFF TO *NOW..?!*

Vandalheim. A Haven for Rogues, Murderers and Worse.

At its Black Heart lies the Death's Door Saloon.

WELCOME
-TO
VANDALHEIM

Evil makes its home here...

... alongside the broken,
and the Fallen from Grace.

This is
One
Such
Man.

A Man
Named --

MONIKA? GO AWAY. HIC!

WELL, IT'S NICE TO SEE THAT YOU HAVEN'T LOST THAT IRRESISTIBLE CHARM OF YOURS --

-- CONSIDERING YOU'VE LOST EVERYTHING ELSE.

NOW GET SERIOUS. I'VE COME TO OFFER YOU SOMETHING...

...A CHANCE TO PROVE YOU HAVEN'T LOST YOUR EDGE.

I'VE BEEN HIRED TO SPRING A PRISONER FROM SKYHOLD. THE INFAMOUS TERRORIST, RYON DEL SOYA.

SNAP

I'VE BEEN GIVEN DETAILED SCHEMATICS OF THE PRISON. SECURITY CODES. SENTRY SHIFTS. I'LL EVEN HAVE ACCESS TO AIR TRANSPORT.

CELL BLOC

ALL YOU'D NEED TO DO IS BREAK A FEW HEADS SHOULD THINGS GET UGLY. TONS OF CASH AND GREAT THRILLS FOR ALL INVOLVED.

SO, TOUGH GUY -- WHAT DO YOU SAY?

SKYHOLD?
HAHAHAHA--
I HAVEN'T LAUGHED IN SO LONG, I THOUGHT I'D FORGOTTEN HOW!

COWARDLY MONGREL! YOU'LL NOT MOCK THE GREAT LADY!

STOP.

THERE'S NO POINT IN BUSTIN' UP A DRUNKEN HAS-BEEN.

STICKS AND STONES...
GLUG GLUG

PATHETIC.

THWAK

IS THIS WHAT YOUR LIFE HAS BECOME?

DO IT, GARRISON.
AND GO TO HELL.

THEN END IT!!
GO ON!!

THUNK

...ALREADY THERE.

HMMZZZT. SHE NEEDS YOUR HELP, KNOLAN.

QUICK -- GET SOME BLANKETS!

And soon, after a much needed rest...

CALIBRETTO TOLD ME EVERYTHING. IT'S OKAY. YOU ARE SAFE HERE WITH US. IN THE MORNING, WE WILL MEET WITH KING VANEER. HE WILL KNOW WHAT TO DO.

I'M SORRY ABOUT YOUR FATHER, *GULLY* -- WE ALL ARE. *ARAMUS* WAS A GREAT, GREAT MAN.

HE'S STILL ALIVE...

I'M SORRY, CHILD. YOU MAY BE RIGHT. PERHAPS THE BOX YOU CARRY MAY HOLD A CLUE.

THE BOX?

C-CAN YOU OPEN IT?

WHAT KIND OF *WIZARD* WOULD I BE, IF I COULDN'T?

CL
CHAK

GET *BACK,* CHILD! WHO KNOWS WHAT MAY BE INSIDE?!

GASP.

Sirene Valley. Three hours past first light.

THIS IS A **BAD** IDEA, CLAVIUS.

MAN... IF THE CAPTAIN FINDS **OUT** ABOUT THIS...

I KNOW, I KNOW. WE'LL CATCH UP WITH THE REST OF THE UNIT LATER. IF WE **HURRY**, THEY WON'T EVEN **NOTICE** WE'RE GONE.

TRUST ME... THIS IS IMPORTANT.

BUT **WHY?** YOU STILL HAVEN'T TOLD ME WHO THIS SO-CALLED **"FRIEND"** OF YOURS IS! WHAT MAKES YOU SO SURE HE CAN HELP US?

HE WAS A SOLDIER, JARREN. MAYBE THE **BEST.** HE TAUGHT ME EVERYTHING I KNOW.

IF ANY-ONE CAN HELP US, IT'S HIM.

LOOK, YOU WAIT HERE. HE'S NOT TOO KEEN ON HAVING VISITORS. IT'LL BE EASIER IF I GO ALONE.

WHATEVER. JUST MAKE IT QUICK.

HELLO? ARE YOU HERE, SIR? IT'S IMPORTANT.

IT'S TOO EARLY IN THE MORNING FOR IMPORTANT MATTERS, CLAVIUS.

YOU'RE IN THE ROYAL GUARD NOW. YOU DON'T HAVE TIME TO BE MY NURSEMAID ANYMORE.

AS YOU CAN SEE, I'M TAKING GREAT CARE OF MYSELF.

I'M GLAD TO SEE THAT YOU'RE DOING SO...WELL. BUT THAT'S NOT WHY I CAME.

IT'S ABOUT ARAMUS.

THERE WAS AN INCIDENT AT HIS HOME LAST NIGHT.

WE DON'T HAVE ALL THE DETAILS, BUT IT'S BEEN CONFIRMED THAT AN *ENTIRE* SQUAD OF OUR MEN WERE SLAUGHTERED, ALONG WITH A FEMALE CIVILIAN.

DAMN. ANY LEADS?

NONE. AND IT GETS WORSE... ARAMUS' DAUGHTER WAS NEVER FOUND. WE BELIEVE THAT SHE MAY HAVE BEEN ABDUCTED...

...OR WORSE.

I KNOW YOU AND ARAMUS WERE CLOSE. THAT'S WHY I CAME, SIR.

YOU ARE NOT POWERLESS IN THIS. RIDE BACK WITH ME...

HELP US FIND THE ONES RESPONSIBLE...

...AND BRING THEM TO JUSTICE.

SIR?

I'M SORRY... I CAN'T HELP YOU. PLEASE GO...

SIR, WAIT!

GO, CLAVIUS. AND NEVER COME BACK.

YOU HEARD THE DRUNK! LET'S GET OUTTA HERE. HMPH... SOME FRIEND.

WHOAH, WHAT A DUMP...

...JARREN...

JARREN, PLEASE!

THIS HOUSE WAS TO BE A GIFT FOR HIS WIFE ON THEIR WEDDING DAY...

"BUT... THERE ISN'T THE SLIGHTEST TRACE OF A WOMAN LIVING HERE. WHAT'D SHE DO?... LEAVE HIM?"

"NO. SHE NEVER GOT TO SEE THE HOUSE -- SHE WAS KILLED ON THEIR WEDDING DAY."

"AFTER THAT, HE SAW NO REASON TO FINISH IT."

"WOULD YOU?"

"YOU SAID HE WAS A SOLDIER..."

"YES. GARRISON. PERHAPS THE GREATEST SWORDSMAN THAT EVER LIVED."

"GARRISON?! YOU'RE TELLING ME THAT GUY WAS *THE* GARRISON?

"IN MANY WAYS, JARREN...

"...HE IS."

"WHOAH. I THOUGHT HE WAS DEAD...

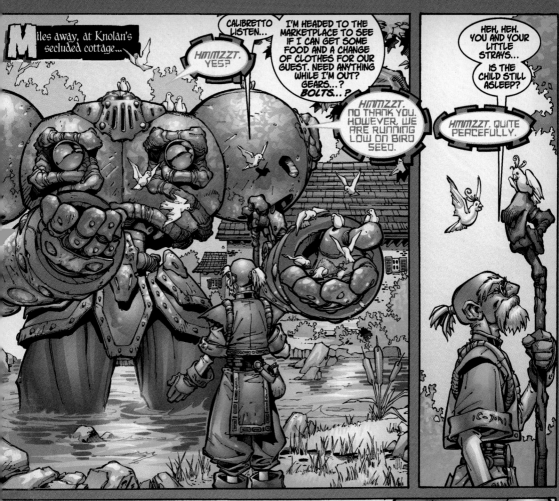

CALIBRETTO LISTEN...

HMMMZZT. YES?

I'M HEADED TO THE MARKETPLACE TO SEE IF I CAN GET SOME FOOD AND A CHANGE OF CLOTHES FOR OUR GUEST. NEED ANYTHING WHILE I'M OUT? GEARS...? *BOLTS...?*

HMMZZT. NO THANK YOU. HOWEVER, WE ARE RUNNING LOW ON BIRD SEED.

HEH, HEH. YOU AND YOUR LITTLE STRAYS... IS THE CHILD STILL ASLEEP?

HMMZZT. QUITE PEACEFULLY.

GOOD! HELLUVA ROUGH NIGHT THAT KID HAD... NOW *LISTEN UP.* THOSE GLOVES AIN'T SOME SENTIMENTAL *HEIRLOOM* LEFT BY DEAR OLD DAD... THEY'RE *EXTREMELY* DANGEROUS.

DON'T LET HER *NEAR* THEM UNTIL I GET BACK. IF I'D KNOWN THEY WERE IN THAT *DAMN* BOX, I NEVER WOULDA OPENED IT!

NIMBUSSS!

BOOF

HMMZZT. THE CHILD... SHE WILL HAVE MANY QUESTIONS. WHAT SHALL I SAY?

NOTHING. WE'LL LET KING VANEER HANDLE THIS. IF THIS ATTACK HAD ANY CONNECTION TO ARAMUS' DISAPPEARANCE, THEN HE NEEDS TO KNOW. JUST REMEMBER... UNTIL I GET BACK... *NO GLOVES!* GOT IT?!

HMMZZT. UNDERSTOOD.

KNOCK
KNOCK

HMMMZT.
KNOLAN...

...DID
YOU FORGET
SOMETHING?

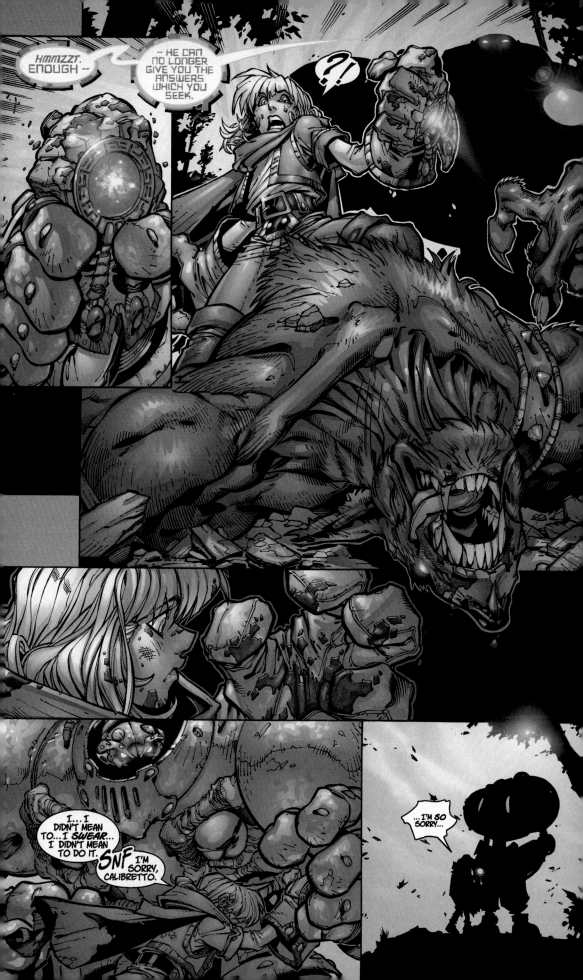

MY HOUSE!

WHAT HAPPENED TO MY HOUSE?!

HMMZZT. PLEASE TRY TO STAY CALM. THE GLOVES, THEY...

THE GLOVES?

THE GLOVES?!

HMMZZT. I WILL EXPLAIN, BUT YOU MUST CALM DOWN! YOUR TEMPER TANTRUM IS AFFECTING THE ENVIRONMENT...

IT'S ABOUT TO AFFECT SOMETHING ELSE

-- AND FAST!

IF YOU DON'T START TALKIN'--

HMMMMMZZZT. THELYCELOTRETURNED ONLYTHISTIMEITBROUGHT ALONGABANDOFGRINNERS WHOMANAGEDTOINCAPACITATE MEMOMENTARILYUSINGSOME SORTOFMAGNETICPULSE CANNON...

OKAY...

...WHICHLEFT THECHILDTO FENDFORHER SELFONLYSHE USEDTHE GLOVES...

OKAY!

...AND PROCEEDED TODESTROY THEIRENTIRE NUMBERASWELL ASTHEHOUSE THEYWERE INWHI...

OKAY!

KTAANG

WHERE IS SHE?!

"*HMMZZT.* SHE IS IN WHAT'S LEFT OF THE SUN ROOM."

A... ARE YOU GOING TO ASK ME TO LEAVE?

NO.

I'M GOING TO ASK YOU TO STAY.

THIS IS YER HOME NOW, FOR AS LONG AS YOU'D LIKE IT TO BE.

THANKS, MISTER KNOLAN.

NOT A PROBLEM, JUST MAKE SURE YOU GET PLENTY OF REST...

YOU HAVE ONE HECK OF A *MESS* TO CLEAN UP IN THE MORNIN'!

ELSEWHERE...

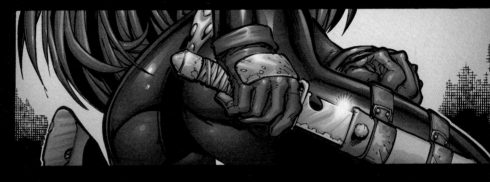

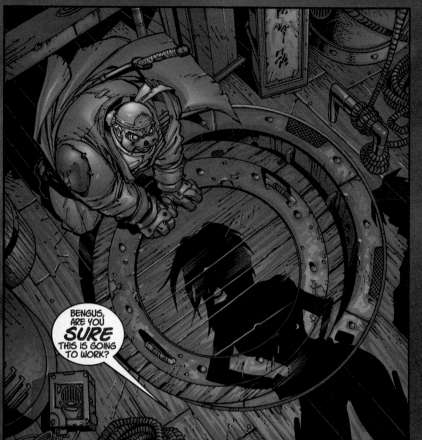

BENGUS, ARE YOU **SURE** THIS IS GOING TO WORK?

LIKE A WELL-OILED MACHINE.

GREAT, UHM... **ONE** MORE QUESTION...

...DO THEY BITE?!

OH, THEY'RE QUITE HARMLESS. UNLESS THEY'RE EXPOSED TO UNNATURAL LIGHT... **THEN** THEY GET **MEAN!**

HEHEHE... SORRY. EH... MAYBE NOW WOULD BE A GOOD TIME TO GO OVER THE PLAN.

West Gun tower.

HAIL, *DUNRIC.* ANYTHING TO REPORT?

NOPE. ALL'S QUIET.

WELL, THIS IS STRANGE. THAT *STRATA RAY* OUT THERE... IT'S BEEN CIRCLING AROUND WITHOUT A RIDER FOR THE LAST TEN MINUTES...

HMM... I'M SURE IT'S JUST A STRAY, BUT I'D BETTER CALL IT IN, JUST IN CASE...

I'M AFRAID I CAN'T LET YOU DO THAT, GENTLEMEN.

WHAT THE...?!

SHIIING

CHUK

CHING

FREEZE!

KL CHAK

SO YOU MUCH AS *BREATHE* AND I'LL...

KRUNCH

YUM.

WH... WHAT THE HELL ARE YOU?

HUNGRY.

One mile below.

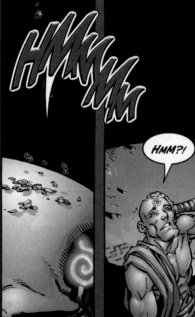

HMM?!

Early the next morning.

Capital City. The largest and most prosperous city in the civil territories.

All of it, ruled by this man...

...King Vaneer

NOW, TELL ME AGAIN OF LAST NIGHT'S OCCURRENCE... THIS TIME, WITHOUT ALL THE *DRAMATICS.*

THIS IS A COUNCIL CHAMBER, NOT A *THEATER.*

MY APOLOGIES, YOUR GRACE. BUT THIS IS A DIRE SITUATION!

LAST NIGHT'S ATTACK ON SKYHOLD VIOLATES EVERY TREATY THAT WE HOLD WITH ISOBAR. TREATIES THAT WERE UNSTABLE TO BEGIN WITH!

MY LORD, THIS COULD WELL BE CONSIDERED AN ACT OF WAR!

WE MUST FIND THE ONES RESPONSIBLE, AND HAND DELIVER THEM TO BARON AVIUS. PERHAPS THIS WOULD RELIEVE TENSIONS...

VERY WELL, GENERAL. YOU HAVE FORTY-EIGHT HOURS.

NOW, IF THAT IS *ALL*... I'M LATE FOR ANOTHER MEETING.

ER... MY LORD. THERE IS STILL THE MATTER OF DUKE RAIMON'S DEATH... ER, MURDER. HOW DO YOU WISH THIS TO BE HANDLED?

THE INVESTIGATION WILL BE CONDUCTED BY MY *MARSHAL PALADINS.* ALL EVIDENCE WILL BE GIVEN DIRECTLY TO ME. IS THAT CLEAR?

AH, MY NEXT MEETING HAS ARRIVED.

"HE IS CALLED THE *MAESTRO.* CAPTAIN OF THE ELITE MILITARY STRIKE-FORCE KNOWN AS THE *MARSHAL PALADINS.*"

I TRUST, GENTLEMEN, THAT YOU WILL NOT MIND...

...LEAVING THE ROOM.

IF I DIDN'T KNOW YOU BETTER, I'D SWEAR YOU ENJOYED THAT.

WITH GARRISON GONE, YOU ARE TRULY THE MOST FEARED MAN IN THE TERRITORIES. WELL, EXCEPT FOR *ME*, PERHAPS.

DO YOU HAVE IT?

YES, HOWEVER... GETTING THIS LIST WAS, SHALL WE SAY... DIFFICULT.

SO LONG AS THE TRAIL OF BODIES CAN'T BE TRACED TO ME... I DON'T CARE.

NOW THEN. OF THIS LIST OF ESCAPED PRISONERS, WHICH SHOULD I BE MOST CONCERNED WITH?

FRANKLY, SIR?

ALL OF THEM.

THEN WE MUST DOUBLE OUR EFFORTS TO FIND ARAMUS. HE WILL BE NEEDED NOW, MORE THAN EVER. HAVE YOU ANY NEWS OF HIS DAUGHTER?

WE ARE STILL SEARCHING.

"WHAT DETAILS WE HAVE ARE SKETCHY AT BEST.

"AS SUCH, HERE IS WHAT WE KNOW."

"WE'VE LEARNED THAT IT WAS A SMALL BAND OF LYCELOTS THAT WAS RESPONSIBLE FOR THE MASSACRE AT ARAMUS' HOME. UNDER THE GUISE OF BOUNTY TRACKERS, THEY WERE ABLE TO GAIN ENTRY, AND SUBSEQUENTLY STEAL THE CHILD."

"WE BELIEVE THAT THEY MAY HAVE BEEN ACTING UNDER SOMEONE ELSES ORDERS. IT IS UNLIKELY THAT THEY WOULD HAVE ATTEMPTED THIS ON THEIR OWN."

"BUT WHO? WHO WOULD DARE...?"

"WHOMEVER IT IS, THEY HAVE NO FEAR OF YOUR MILITARY STRENGTH. THE NATURE OF SUCH AN ATTACK LEADS ME TO BELIEVE THAT IT WAS PERSONAL."

"REGARDLESS, I WANT THAT CHILD FOUND AT ONCE! FOR ALL WE KNOW..."

CALIBRETTO! I'VE GOT THE CHILD! SHE'S OKAY!

HMMZZT. GET HER TO SAFETY...

...I WILL DEAL WITH THIS VERMIN!

VRRT

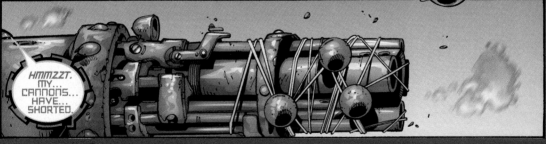

HMMZZT. MY... CANNONS... HAVE... SHORTED.

FRROOMMM

ENOUGH! I HAVE NOT KILLED A MAN IN MANY YEARS, BUT I WILL IF I MUST, TO PROTECT THIS CHILD!

THEN OLD MAN...

KRAKA BOOOM

NO...

TH-THEY'RE ALL DEAD... THE CAPTAIN, EVERYONE... DEAD!

DO NOT GRIEVE FOR YOUR FRIENDS. THEY HAVE GONE TO A BETTER PLACE, FREE FROM THE TREACHERY AND INDIGNATION OF THIS WORLD.

YOU-YOU'RE CRAZY TO COME BACK HERE. VANEER HAS HUNDREDS OF MEN DEFENDING THE CITY.

IRONIC, ISN'T IT? THAT HUNDREDS SHALL DIE... FOR THE SINS OF A SINGLE ONE.

HUCHT!

CHUK

THE ONE MAN EVER TO DEFEAT ME...

...AND THAT'S WHEN 'BRETTO SAVED ME. HE AND KNOLAN HAVE TAKEN GREAT CARE OF ME!

KNOLAN?! WELL... IT SEEMS I OWE YOU AND YOUR FRIENDS AN APOLOGY. AFTER I HEARD ABOUT WHAT HAPPENED, I JUST WANTED TO MAKE SURE YOU WERE SAFE.

FATHER STILL TALKED ABOUT YOU AFTER YOU LEFT.

HE EVEN TOLD ME ONCE, THAT HE LOVED YOU LIKE YOU WERE HIS OWN SON.

YES, YOUR FATHER AND I WERE VERY CLOSE...

REALLY? THEN WHY DID YOU GO AWAY?! DIDN'T YOU KNOW IT WOULD BREAK HIS HEART?!

I STILL CAN'T GET OVER HOW MUCH YOU'VE GROWN! YOU MUST BE EIGHT NOW!

I'M GOING TO BE TEN-AND-A HALF SOON.

IT'S BEEN... THAT LONG?

GULLY, I...

IF FATHER THOUGHT YOU WERE IN TROUBLE, HE WOULD'VE MOVED MOUNTAINS TO FIND YOU! AFTER YOU STOPPED COMING BY, HE EVEN SENT PEOPLE TO CHECK ON YOU, AND MAKE SURE YOU WERE OKAY! BUT, YOU... DID YOU EVER EVEN TRY TO LOOK FOR HIM?

YOU NEVER CARED ABOUT HIM AT ALL...ABOUT ANY OF US!

GULLY, PLEASE!

...

NO! LEAVE ME ALONE!

TWENTY CASUALTIES AT OUTPOST ZETA. TWENTY SENSELESS DEATHS. IT'S OBVIOUS THOSE ROGUES WERE TRYING TO GET MY ATTENTION. NO DOUBT THEY'VE MADE IT INTO THE CITY BY NOW.

IT CAN ONLY BE A MATTER OF TIME BEFORE THEY STRIKE. BUT UNTIL WE KNOW WHAT WE'RE UP AGAINST, SENDING MORE MEN WOULD BE LIKE SENDING LAMBS TO THE SLAUGHTER.

THAT'S QUITE A PREDICAMENT YOU'VE GOTTEN YOURSELF INTO...

...I'M IN A POSITION TO MAKE IT MUCH WORSE.

WHO...?!

DO NOT SPEAK! MERELY LISTEN, FOR I HAVE COME TO MAKE YOU AN OFFER. ONE THAT MAY JUST SAVE YOUR PRECIOUS CITY.

OUR DEMANDS ARE QUITE REASONABLE. THE MARSHAL PALADIN WHO TORMENTED US, WHO HUNTED US DOWN LIKE DOGS -- TURN HIM OVER TO US, AND YOUR CITY WILL BE SPARED.

ONE MAN, FOR THE LIVES OF COUNTLESS INNOCENTS, SOUNDS TO ME LIKE A BARGAIN.

YOU KNOW I CAN'T DO THAT.

THEN IF YOU'LL EXCUSE ME, YOUR HIGHNESS...

While, at the city...

FINALLY, WE'RE...! **HERE?!** KNOLAN! *THE CITY!*

EITHER THIS CITY IS UNDER ATTACK, OR VANEER'S GOT ONE *HECK* OF A FIREWORKS DISPLAY!

LET'S GO!

And soon...

HMMZZT. KNOLAN, THERE IS DEFINITELY A *HOSTILE* PRESENCE WITHIN THE CITY.

I THINK WE'VE GOT *THAT* PART FIGURED OUT, SHELL-SHORTS! HOW'S ABOUT A *WHO,* AND *WHY?!*

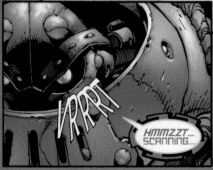

VRRRT

HMMZZT... SCANNING...

CLK

HMMZZT. THE ATTACKS ALL SEEM TO COME FROM A *SINGLE, HIGH-LEVEL MAGIC USER.*

MAGIC?! THAT'S *YOUR* DEPARTMENT, MR. KNOLAN! YOU'VE *GOTTA* DO SOMETHING!

WHAT DO I LOOK LIKE, KID? SOME KIND OF *SUPER-HERO?!*

I DON'T *SAVE* THE DAY, I JUST TRY TO *ENJOY* IT!

THOUGH AT THIS RATE, I MAY NOT HAVE MANY LEFT!

POWER

The word rips through her mind as though it were fired from a cannon.

Her Name, her very identity, lost in the wake of its Fury.

She is left with a **single** memory.

A memory of the day she Ceased to Exist.

She was a Grave Robber, a common Rogue.

Her companions had unearthed the burial site of a long dead ruler. Countless treasures filled the cavernous hollows of the tomb's black heart.

She was drawn to a strange Golden Bracelet which seemed to call her.

"**POWER**" it said,

"**FREE ME, AND THE POWER SHALL BE YOURS.**"

But that power, she soon learned, came at Great Price.

The cost was her very Soul.

I... STOPPED YOUR HEART. I SAW YOU DIE!

DAMN YOU, OLD MAN, *SHOW YOURSELF!*

MY HEART'S BEEN BEATING FOR A *LOOONG* TIME, KID. I'VE SEEN *EVERY* TRICK IN THE BOOK.

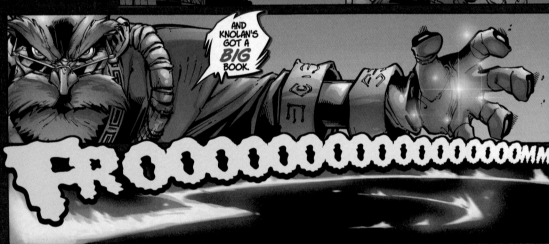

AND KNOLAN'S GOT A *BIG* BOOK.

FR OOOOOOOOOOOOOOOOOOOOOMM

WHA?! WHAT'S *THIS?*

I'D TRY NOT TO MAKE ANY SUDDEN MOVEMENTS IF I WERE YOU!

I'M *NOT* FALLING FOR *ANOTHER* OF YOUR SILLY GAMES!

I WAS HOPIN YOU'D SA THAT.

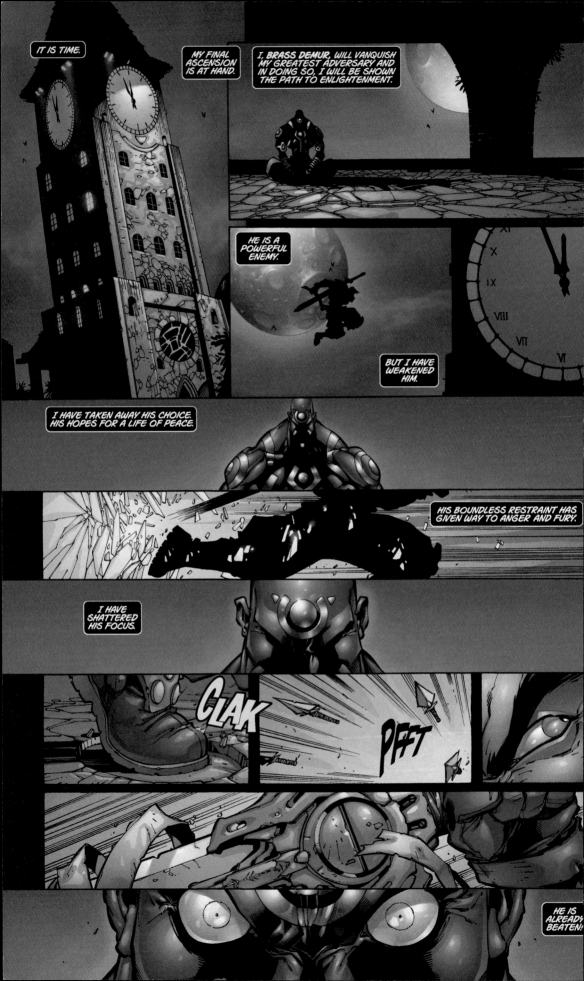

The following story appears courtesy of *Frank Frazetta Fantasy Illustrated.*

A QUIET MOMENT...

CALIBRETTO
OUTLAW WARGOLEM.

GULLY
PINT-SIZED JUGGERNAUGHT.

WHATCHA READIN'?

HMMTZT -- AN INTERESTING TEXT ON AVIAN HUNTING METHODOLOGY -- WRITTEN BY AN ISOBARIAN NATURALIST. IT IS FILLED WITH THE MOST FASCINATING OBSERVATIONS -- CARE TO HEAR A FEW?

UHH -- NO, THAT'S OKAY.

KNOLAN
SUMMONER SUPREME.

SHHHK
SHHHK
SHHHK

-- AND
GARRISON
LEGENDARY SWORDSMAN.

GARRISON? WHATCHA DOIN' WITH THAT ROCK?

-- MAYBE IT COULD GET RID OF MY IMPERFECTIONS. I'M NEW TO THIS HERO STUFF -- SOMETIMES I FEEL... OUT OF PLACE.

SKILL IS A DULL STONE THAT GAINS EDGE AS TIME PASSES.

THIS "ROCK" ALLOWS ME TO CLEANSE MY SWORD ERASING THE SLIGHTEST IMPERFECTIONS FROM ITS BLADE.

WISH I HAD ONE OF THOSE STONES --

COURAGE IS SOMETHING THAT CAN'T BE TAUGHT-- AND YOU GULLY, ARE BLESSED WITH BOTH.

REALLY? WERE YOU ALWAYS THIS TOUGH, EVEN AS A KID?!

IT'S NOT ALWAYS
WHO'S THE TOUGHEST,
GULLY. AS A MARTIAL
PALADIN, I'VE BEEN
TRAINED IN ALL FORMS
OF COMBAT.

-- AND HAVE
ENDURED ENDLESS
HOURS OF PHYSICAL
CONDITIONING -- BUT
GOING WITH YOUR
GUT WAS NOT IN THE
CURRICULUM -- IN FACT,
IT WAS FROWNED
UPON. MY FINAL
TRAINING MISSION
WAS TO HUNT DOWN
AND KILL A RAMPAGING
BEAST CALLED THE
LUNDARA. DURING OUR
BATTLE, CERTAIN
PIECES DIDN'T SEEM
TO FIT -- SO I
TRUSTED MY
INSTINCTS, AND
LOWERED MY GUARD,
STOPPING THE FIGHT.
THE MONSTER WE HAD
THOUGHT HIM TO BE,
BUT A PEACEFUL,
INTELLIGENT CREATURE
WHOSE ACTIONS
WERE GREATLY
MISUNDERSTOOD.
I WAS REPRIMANDED
FOR DISOBEYING
ORDERS -- BUT THAT
DAY, I ALSO *GAINED*
SOMETHING. TO THIS
DAY, THE LUNDARA
REMAINS MY MOST
CHERISHED AND
TRUSTED FRIEND. SO
YOU SEE, GULLY,
KNOWING *WHEN* TO
FIGHT IS AS IMPORTANT
AS KNOWING *HOW*
TO FIGHT!

HMMZZT... YES, THIS IS TRUE -- HOWEVER, MY STORY IS FAR MORE TRAGIC.

MY BRETHREN AND I WERE CREATED TO BE GREAT ENGINES OF WAR. OUR TASK -- TO ERADICATE THE THREAT OF INVASION BY AN ARMY OF POWERFUL MARAUDERS. SOON AFTER OUR VICTORY, THE VERY PEOPLE WE WERE BUILT TO PROTECT, BEGAN TO FEAR OUR VAST DESTRUCTIVE CAPABILITIES. WE WERE HUNTED DOWN -- DESTROYED ON SIGHT. EVERY LAST ONE OF US, DRIVEN TO EXTINCTION. IF NOT FOR KNOLAN'S KINDNESS IN OFFERING ME SHELTER, I TOO WOULD HAVE PERISHED. IN THE MANY YEARS FOLLOWING THAT SENSELESS WAR, I HAVE LEARNED LESSON -- MEANINGLESS DESTRUCTION IS A WASTE OF PRECIOUS LIFE. ONE MUST REPLACE WHAT ONE HAS DESTROYED. THIS IS THE CODE I NOW LIVE BY.

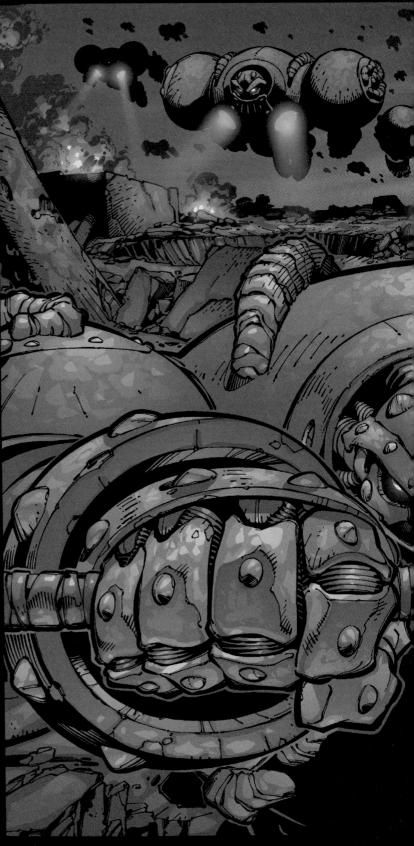

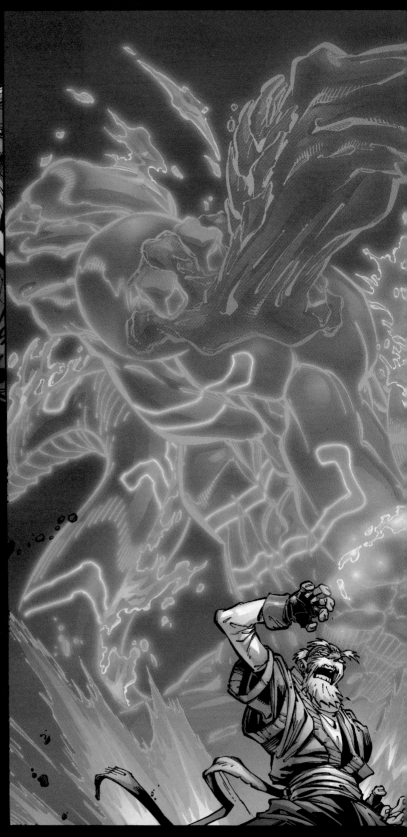

-- WE'VE ALL BEEN THROUGH THE FIRE -- SOME, MORE TIMES THAN OTHERS. HEY, BEIN' 500 YEARS OLD, I'VE CLOCKED MORE TIME ON THE BATTLEFIELD THAN ALL O' YA PUT TOGETHER! NOW, I'VE NEVER SERVED ANY SORT OF REGIME, OR HAD ANY SPECIAL TRAINING IN THE ANCIENT ARTS OF BUTT-KICKIN', BUT BE IT POWER-MAD DICTATORS, OR RIVAL MAGES WHO DIDN'T LIKE THE WAY I PRACTICED MY MAGIC -- TROUBLE ALWAYS HAD A WAY O' *FINDIN'* ME. YOU SHOULDN'T BE INSECURE ABOUT YER LACK OF PLAYIN' TIME GULLY -- THE SWORDSMAN'S RIGHT -- YOU'VE GOT WHAT IT TAKES. YOU COME FROM A STRONG STOCK.

B

F

J

CALIBRETTO

CONTINUE THE ADVENTURE WITH THESE OTHER BOOKS FROM CLIFFHANGER, WILDSTORM AND DC:

COLLECTIONS

Danger Girl: The Dangerous Collection #1
HARTNELL/CAMPBELL/GARNER

Danger Girl: The Dangerous Collection #2
HARTNELL/CAMPBELL/GARNER

Darkchylde
QUEEN/VARIOUS

Divine Right: Collected Edition #1
LEE/WILLIAMS

Divine Right: Collected Edition #2
LEE/WILLIAMS

Divine Right: Collected Edition #3
LEE/WILLIAMS

Crimson: Loyalty & Loss
AUGUSTYN/RAMOS/HOPE

Gen13
CHOI/LEE/CAMPBELL/GARNER

Gen13: #13 ABC
CHOI/LEE/CAMPBELL/GARNER

Gen13: Bootleg Vol. 1
VARIOUS WRITERS AND ARTISTS

Gen13: Grunge the Movie
WARREN

Gen13: Interactive Plus
VARIOUS WRITERS AND ARTISTS

Gen13: Starting Over
CHOI/LEE/CAMPBELL/
GARNER/WILLIAMS

Kurt Busiek's Astro City: Life in the Big City
BUSIEK/ANDERSON

Kurt Busiek's Astro City: Confession
BUSIEK/ANDERSON/BLYBERG

Kurt Busiek's Astro City: Family Album
BUSIEK/ANDERSON/BLYBERG

Leave It to Chance: Shaman's Rain
ROBINSON/SMITH

Leave It to Chance: Trick or Threat
ROBINSON/SMITH/FREEMAN

Wetworks: Rebirth
PORTACIO/CHOI/WILLIAMS

WildC.A.T.s: Compendium
VARIOUS WRITERS AND ARTISTS

WildC.A.T.s: Gang War
MOORE/VARIOUS

WildC.A.T.s: Gathering of Eagles
CLAREMONT/LEE/WILLIAMS

WildC.A.T.s: Homecoming
MOORE/VARIOUS

WildC.A.T.s/X-Men
VARIOUS WRITERS AND ARTISTS

WildStorm Archives: Gen13
VARIOUS WRITERS AND ARTISTS

WS Fine Arts: The Gallery Collection
VARIOUS ARTISTS

WildStorm Rising
WINDSOR SMITH/VARIOUS

OTHER COLLECTIONS OF INTEREST

Art of Chiodo
CHIODO

The Batman Adventures: Mad Love
DINI/TIMM

Batman: The Dark Knight Returns
MILLER/VARLEY/JANSON

Batman: Faces
WAGNER

Batman: The Killing Joke
MOORE/BOLLAND/HIGGINS

Batman: Year One
MILLER/MAZZUCCHELLI/LEWIS

Camelot 3000
BARR/BOLLAND

The Golden Age
ROBINSON/SMITH

Green Lantern: A New Dawn
MARZ/BANKS/TANGHAL

JLA: New World Order
MORRISON/PORTER/DELL

JLA: Rock of Ages
MORRISON/PORTER/DELL/VARIOUS

JLA: Strength in Numbers
VARIOUS WRITERS AND ARTISTS

JLA/ WildC.A.T.s
MORRISON/SEMEIKS/CONRAD

Kingdom Come
WAID/ROSS

Ronin
MILLER

Watchmen
MOORE/GIBBONS

ARCHIVE EDITIONS

All Star Comics Archives Vols. 1-4
VARIOUS WRITERS AND ARTISTS

The Flash Archives Vol. 1
VARIOUS WRITERS AND ARTISTS

Green Lantern Archives Vol. 1
VARIOUS WRITERS AND ARTISTS

Golden Age Green Lantern Archiv Vol. 1
VARIOUS WRITERS AND ARTISTS

Justice League of America Archive Vols. 1-4
VARIOUS WRITERS AND ARTISTS

Legion of Super-Heroes Archives Vols. 1-8
VARIOUS WRITERS AND ARTISTS

Plastic Man Archives Vol. 1
VARIOUS WRITERS AND ARTISTS

For the nearest comics shop carrying collected editions and monthly titles from DC Comics, call 1-888-COMIC BOOK.